Black Sheep Rebel Girl

The Almost True Tales,

Thoughts, and Observations

of a Lifelong…

Black Sheep Rebel Girl

A Collection of the Stuff in My Head

By Rachel Hutcheson

This book is dedicated to the outsiders, the fringe walkers, the never-quite-fit-ins, the underdogs, the long-shots, the late bloomers, the dark horses, the free spirit black sheep rebels, and my mom.

Truth

Everything I write is either biographical, autobiographical, semi-autobiographical, or made up.

I wear a pirate patch so other pirates can find me.

Last Tuesday, I saw a coyote sitting on the hood of a car reading a Harlequin romance novel.

If life is not a dream, what is it?

If a dream is not life, what is it?

If we all sat down and ate a hot bowl of oatmeal together, a hot bowl of oatmeal loaded with butter and brown sugar, we might have world peace.

That's all I really have to say about that.

Blown Off a Star

I wasn't born in this universe.

I was blown off a star on a blustery day and buffered my landing by stuffing clouds into my clothes before plopping into a vat of freshly puffed marshmallows ten miles east of Kathmandu.

The marshmallows were undeniably springy, and I bounced back up 1,700 miles before sliding down a rainbow into Lake Michigan.

I stripped the color off a rainbow that day, and you can still see the violet, green, yellow, and red stripes on the bottoms of my feet.

Me, too

You know when you are being yourself and someone will say, "You're so funny," but you know they don't really think you're funny? They think you're weird, but they say *funny* because they don't know what else to say?

Me, too.

You know when you feel like your badass self and no one else's ideas or thoughts of who you are, are stuck to you or influencing you, and you feel powerful and unstoppable?

Me, too.

You know when you realize everybody in the entire world is crazy? And you notice even super smart people are whack and your friends are whack and your family is whack and you can't come up with a single name of somebody who isn't whack? But you don't even care because life is awesome, and you are just happy to be alive?

Me, too.

You know when you look at the sky and notice how beautiful the clouds are and you have to say it out loud? You have to say, "Wow, the clouds are so beautiful?"

Me, too. Like, every time I see a cloud.

I'm for Laughter

I'm for laughter, happily ever after. It doesn't matter who, it doesn't matter what. When and where do not matter, I'm for laughter.

I'm for laughter loud enough to make people think, "What an asshole, shut up!" I'm for laughter at the wrong time, at funerals, board meetings, during sex, flat-tires, hurricanes, and shipwrecks.

I'm for laughter stopping us from falling off the last step into solemn oblivion. I'm for laughter as the recognition of the joke that life can sometimes be.

I'm for laughter from the heart, laughter that lifts one's spirit so high everything looks funny and you can't get serious about life anymore because you get the joke.

I'm for the giddy laughter coming from the small feet people who pitter-patter.

I'm for laughter when the money's in the red and losing is all the chatter. I'm for laughter for no reason at all or just because it feels good, a good hearty laugh like a good laugh should.

I'm for laughter with friends who make you crack up no matter what they say.

I'm for laughter is the best medicine and you got to take it every day like a painkiller. Only it doesn't just dull the pain, it makes the pain go away: so long pain, you lose to laughter.

Uncontrollable, cheek-hurting, spit-spewing, pee-inducing, stomach-pain-bringing, hey thank you for making me laugh like a jackass. I don't need a single thing, because I got you, laughter.

Laughter is what I'm after. I'm for laughter.

Naked Women

Renada draws all her masterpieces on roads made of blacktop and boulevards lined with begonias. Before she begins, she places three orange pylons at each end of the block she is working on. Then she covers the asphalt with pastel drawings of plump naked laughing women lying on red velvet lounge chairs and purple sofas. People ask what the drawings mean, but Renada never explains her work.

Every street she claims brings hordes of new and old fans who watch her anoint the pavement. Money is offered, and bribing is resorted to in an effort to persuade Renada to paint on canvas. But Renada has no interest in canvas. She says she finds her grace only after she completes each piece and rain comes to mix the colors into little rivers on the street.

You see, Renada considers herself first and foremost a street photographer. She wears an old sea captain's coat while she captures pictures of her paintings disappearing in the downpour.

Each year, she puts out a coffee table book of her fading street art. Her books have titles such as *It's Only Good When It's Gone* and *Die Painting Die.*

On the very last page of each book, she prints the same sentence in a tiny, almost unreadable, font:

"Everybody needs a gimmick. This one's mine. Find your own."

If

If I didn't believe in rainbows,

would I still see them?

If I didn't believe in love,

would I ever find it?

If I found a million dollars,

would I turn it into the police

or would I know better by now?

Tennessee Williams

If I were Tennessee Williams, dialogue would drip from my lips wrapped in orange blossom honey and cayenne pepper.

Words like *dissension, deception, and liquor* would leap off my pages and throw my characters into reckless passion and wild despair.

You would feel obligated to nominate me for literary awards. After I won, you would invite me to speak about the wonders of me.

If I were Tennessee Williams.

The Edge of the Universe

People said I was some kind of crazy, thinking I could hang on to a dream I'd had since I was a little kid. But I knew I couldn't expect somebody who has never rode a comet across the sky to understand something as astral as a dream.

They can't see that far that's all, they just don't have the vision.

But it's not glasses they need, it's soul. The kind of soul that keeps your heart beating when everything you ever loved is lost. Soul that makes you see the devastating beauty in tragedy and shallow tragedy in beauty.

Soul that goes so deep you can feel water flowing through it all the way down to the center of the earth. I'm talking soul so incredibly alive it can yank you right out of the desert of dead dreams and pump the breath back into lifeless hope.

I got soul. That's how I made it all the way out to the edge of the universe, all universes.

See, I had it in my mind for some time that I wanted to find what people call the "Edge of the World." In fact, I wanted to find the edge of all worlds, the whole game. Once I get something in my head, I don't give up easily. After an extensive search, I acquired a space-travel vehicle I felt would take me to my destination.

I purchased the rocket from an old man in Billings, Montana, right off Craigslist. He'd been working on building a space-travel machine since the 1970s and finally created one that worked.

It was made out of a Ski-Doo snowmobile and he stuck all kinds of rocket blasters, navigational devices, and long-distance travel instruments on it. Then he heat-proofed it, cold-proofed it, and stuck a lid over the whole thing.

It was quite simple to navigate and fairly comfortable for what it was. Plus, he included a space suit, which made me look like a giant tuna. The listing said no haggling. So, I paid the full price with a money order as requested and set off to find the edge of the universe.

Within a week I was up near the first star on the handle of the Big Dipper. After a few more weeks I was well out of the Milky Way altogether.

Sometimes, there was only darkness as I traveled. But sometimes, I would rocket past planets and vistas I'd never read about in any book. I saw planets that looked as clear as a glass ball on a Christmas tree. I passed planets in the shapes of squares, diamonds, and triangles.

Eventually, I came upon an area I named the Space Lands. There I traveled through the Land of Floating Rock and the Land of Lopsided Mountains, where I saw mountains sitting in space with no planet beneath them. I passed through the Land of Shimmer, which was filled with a silvery glitter dust that covered my ship like a thick blanket of sand.

Eight thousand miles later I tried to wash it off by flying back and forth under one tiny cloud I found in the Land of Rain.

Just after I passed through the Land of Turn Back Now, I saw an enormous ring suspended in space. When I got a little closer, I could see it was actually a sign that read "Edge of the Universe" in blazing gold letters.

At that point, my Spaceship began to shake and the nearer I got to the sign the more my Ski-Doo spaceship shook. I don't mean back and forth either, I mean tiny vibrations as if the particles it was made of were starting to separate.

When I got up close to the ring, I saw it was stamped with an official bright red "Edge of the Universe" seal. Somebody else had arrived before me and scratched "If you don't believe it stick your finger through the ring" into the red veneer covering the seal.

Now, I didn't go all that way just to see a big "Edge of the Universe" sign. So, I tightened my space suit, opened my hatch, and anchored my ship with indestructible rope to the *U* in universe and floated down toward the middle of the ring.

Then I stuck my left index finger through the center and when I pulled it back, there was no finger there at all. It wasn't burnt off or pulled off. It was as if it had never existed, it just disappeared.

I knew at that moment I would disappear too if I went through the ring to the other side. In fact, the longer I stayed there, the stronger I got the feeling that *nothing is real* and the idea *you don't exist* kept pressing into my mind. It made me think I was going crazy, so I jumped back into my spaceship and headed home.

I found the "Edge of the Universe" alright, and that's exactly what it is, the EDGE OF THE UNIVERSE and the entrance to no universe at all. The entrance to nothing. My missing index finger is proof.

But it was one incredible adventure. It was my "To be or not to be" moment. My opportunity to decide if I wanted to be or not. If I wanted to exist or not.

I guess you know which one I chose.

Head Trip

Do you ever wonder who made the universe?

And if you think "no one made it" and it was just here, do you wonder how it got here?

And if you think God made it, do you wonder who made God?

And if you think that no one made God because he was somehow just here, do you wonder what he did before he got here? Before he made the universe?

Was he bored? Where did he live?

Does he spend his time watching us now or does he have friends to hang out with?

And if you think there is no God and we just came from mud and chemicals; do you wonder how the mud got here? Do you ever wonder who made the mud?

Angels

Even angels have eating disorders these days. It's not easy to work in heaven anymore, what with all the reality TV shows and the Victoria's Secret ad campaigns they are streaming up there. An angel can't just be an angel anymore.

Now she's got to be a fucking supermodel, too.

One More Me, Too

Do you ever catch a shadow, a glimpse of someone passing by from the corner of your eye when there is no one else in the house but you? Me, too. I think it's a time thing. A colliding of one time with another. I think it's a glitch, some bubble in the time stream. Like 50 years ago showed up today and I saw it. I don't think you're supposed to see it, but when you do you know it's true. It's either that or a ghost—which is cool, too. Can you give me a *Me, too* on that? Or does that just freak you out?

(Use the space below to enter your reply.)

The New York City Elephant

One afternoon I saw a baby elephant swimming in the pond in Central Park. He didn't appear to be with anyone, so when he got out of the water, I walked up to him and asked if he had a place to stay in the city. I didn't open my mouth when I asked him. I thought-asked him and he thought-answered me back, saying that he did not have a place to stay.

So, we walked side by side down Eighth Avenue to my apartment on 21st Street. Nobody said a word. No one asked a question or even took a picture. You know how New Yorkers are, you can quite literally walk with an elephant down the sidewalk and no one would even be surprised.

Once we arrived at my old brownstone, it was obvious this baby elephant wasn't going to find my thin, four-room railroad apartment comfortable. So, we walked straight down the hall and outside to the garden patio in the back. All the buildings on my block share a courtyard, and he has been living back there ever since. He likes the trees, and the fountains, and the vegetable gardens, and the cats, and the benches.

Everyone gave up their courtyard space and he has the run of the inside of a whole city block. We built a heated shelter for the winters, and he paints on canvas and works out on a giant treadmill when he is not rolling in mud or peeking in windows.

At first, I tried to get him to go to a preserve, but he said he didn't want to go. He said he likes New York City and that's where he wants to live. He told me that for a long time he didn't even know he was an elephant.

He thought he was a beautiful girl with long legs, and that he had aspirations of dancing with the Rockettes at Radio City Music Hall. When he finally realized he was an elephant and not a girl with long legs, he decided he would at least be part of the city, and so he stayed.

He likes visitors. You can go and see him anytime you want. Some people charge to go through their building to take a peek. But I never did, I always let people come and look for free. He likes people and loves to talk. You'd be surprised how easy it is to talk to an elephant.

Some people don't want to talk to him. They don't trust the words they hear him putting into their head. But I found him to be gentle and interesting.

We used to talk about Gandhi and Jesus and why we think the sun continues to burn. We used to take long walks at three in the morning down to the Village and up to the Met. I still get holiday cards from him. That's how I know he is still there.

If you ever end up in the city, let me know. I'll make sure you get to meet him.

The Ride

We ride our broomsticks across the sky. It's always nice when there are clouds because we don't have to worry about bullets or missiles coming at us.

Not a single soul can see we are up there.

People call us witches. People say a lot of things. But when you can fly on a broom you don't really care what people say. You just try to enjoy the ride.

Being an Asshole

Have you ever looked back and noticed different times in your life when you were an asshole?

I have.

I have looked back and realized that I have been an asshole more times than I would like to remember. Of course, I didn't see it at the time, so I went ahead and did my asshole thing.

However, I do believe if I would have seen it while I was doing it, I would have thought, *Oh, don't do that, that's being an asshole.*

Which, I hope, would have made me stop.

One of the main benefits for me, about noticing my own assholeness, is when I see someone else being an asshole. It might piss me off at first, but then I usually come around to thinking, *No big deal, I too have been an asshole on numerous occasions,* and that chills me out.

That's all I really have to say about being an asshole.

Public Service Announcement #1

If you see a cat in a window you have to take his picture. If you don't take his picture, it's completely possible that he will immediately get a hairball he has to cough up or you will get a hairball you'll have to cough up.

Now, let's say there is a cat in a window, and you don't see him. Or you do see him, but you don't have a camera with you.

Well, then this rule does not apply.

Otherwise, it is strictly in force. I don't make the rules. I just try to keep people informed so we can all live hairball-free.

Like

It's sad to be so sad, I want to tell her. It won't ever make you happy, I want to say. It won't ever cure your pain. It won't make you laugh or help you fall in love. Don't feed the sadness, I want to say to her. But truthfully, she won't understand. She told me she likes the sadness. It gives her something to talk about. So, I just hit "Like" and move on.

Modern-Day Pixies

We found the woods where they have always been, sitting at the edge of the tall peppermint grass and patches of Queen Anne's lace. Once we began walking through the pines and giant oak, it was easy to spot the pixies hiding on the branches and under the green leaves.

It's not that the pixies weren't perfectly hidden from view, they were. I mean, they blended into the trees with no reflection or shadow. Their problem was, they were noisy. Maybe not all of them, but the *shut ups* we heard from one of the pixies were louder than the couple of big-mouthed pixies he was trying to get to be quiet.

Every time one pixie would say, "Shut up," another one would say, "No, you shut up."

This went back and forth 15 times. I have never seen a more disorganized and disorderly band of pixies anywhere. One sang "This Little Light of Mine" like he was Stevie Wonder during the whole encounter. There is absolutely no doubt they wanted to be seen. I couldn't help laughing until one landed on my head and pulled my hair. I had to reach up and pull him off me.

He was not happy when I held him up in the air by his shirt collar. I told him they need to get it together because most people won't be as cool about pixies as me. I explained that some people will try to catch them in nets, bring them home, and keep them in waterless fishbowls like pets. That doesn't include government agencies showing up who will want to cage and dissect you I told them.

The pixie told me I was stupid and then he ordered me to bring them an iPhone and a TV with HBO. He said they are sick of being pixies and living in the woods, and if I like it so much, we should trade places. I didn't know what to say after that. So, I faked confidence and told him to watch himself or soon he won't have to worry about living in the woods or anywhere else for that matter.

He must not have believed me, or he didn't care, because then he screamed in his tiny pixie voice, "Bring us the iPhone or we will find out where you live and move in."

So now I have 7 pixies living in my house. They watch my HBO, eat my food, and boss me around. I think I might be the only one among us who cares about their future, and they basically shit all over me.

They told me all the goblins have left the woods. They said they found some better living arrangement and moved on. Better? I laughed, "What could be better than being a magical creature and living in the woods?"

"Budweiser," a pixie said, and then he burped.

Even magical creatures don't want to be magical anymore.

What will happen when they all become just like us?

Paper

Sometimes,

I wish I could make money.

In my basement.

On a machine.

Out of paper.

Jack

A couple of hours ago I found an enormous leaf. I wish you could be here in person to see how big this leaf is. It would completely cover a VW van. You could actually fold it around a giant redwood tree like you were making a chicken wrap.

I had to go up to the fifth floor of a building and hang out a window just to get a full shot of the monster. It did not fall from a tree. I watched it fall from the clear blue sky.

At first, I thought it was a balloon, but the closer it got to the ground, the bigger it grew. When it did finally land, I started to wonder about its previous location. Where did it come from?

My best guess is we should all start looking for Jack and ask him where he has been. I think we deserve to know in advance if a giant might be making his way down to earth.

Words

Don't you think it's awesome that *awesome* is a word?

(Use the space below to give your answer and to write down words you think are awesome.)

Robin Hood

When someone says to me, don't you wish you were Robin Hood?

I say, "It's nice to wish I was Robin Hood. It's nice to think about stealing from the rich and giving to the poor.

But if Robin Hood was a real person and if I were him, I would be dead.

So, no, I do not wish I was Robin Hood."

Paraguay

I first became interested in the art of love spells when I was an exchange student in Paraguay during my sophomore year of college. The university offered a class in Ancient Charms and I thought, "Why not?" I didn't believe in charms at the time, but I found out how wrong I was on the second day of class when we began reading about all the famous affairs that began with an undeniable love spell.

Did you know Antony bribed one of Cleopatra's servant girls to pour a passion potion into Cleo's bath an hour before she and Antony met for the first time?

Did you know that during the early part of the 20th century, seven out of 10 marriages in the USA came about after one of the soon-to-be spouses looked into a mirror smeared with first-day-of-spring sun glitter?

Did you know that this magic sun glitter falls on a six-by-four-inch spot in North Dakota each year on March 23 for three minutes starting at 10:07 a.m.?

Did you know that sun glitter is considered one of the most amorous of all amorous ingredients?

Perhaps you have seen couples who do not seem to match in your mind. The man is crusty, and the woman is young and pretty. It's quite easy to see the whys and wherefores of these matches if you understand the ability of a spell to bring out the true *inner beauty* of a person.

Contrary to popular belief, a spell does not make a person fall in love. A spell brings the love out of a person so that they can actually love the person they are meant to love.

Some spells can even make an entire country, and I am talking about hundreds of millions of people, fall in love with one single person.

For example, and you may find this hard to believe because you might be bewitched by this woman. The spell she cast is highly infectious and continues to spread to this very day.

I am speaking of Marilyn Monroe. It is not known that she wasn't incredibly beautiful and would not be considered a sex symbol by most people if she had not cast a spell on the world when she was 15.

What occurred as a fluke of nature turned her into an international star. Marilyn didn't even know she had cast the spell until years later when she was studying the art of love spells and realized what she had done.

You see, when Marilyn was 15 years old, she was chanting "Everyone loves me" over and over into her bathroom mirror. Her heart had recently been broken, and she was trying to wish the pain away.

It just so happens that at the very same time she was chanting to herself, the first atomic bomb test took place in New Mexico (The Manhattan Project). When that bomb went off, it poured so much bitterness and hate into the world, the vibrations of Earth started searching for something innocent. The first drop of innocence it contacted was Norma Jean chanting "Everyone loves me."

When the vibrations of Earth connected with her, the radioactive waves from the atomic bomb were counterbalanced by the stronger wave of innocent love that Marilyn was sending out into the world. It was at that moment she became a true magnet for beauty and love in the universe.

This was years before anyone even knew who she was, and all because life can only take so much pain and cruelty before it must send something beautiful back into the world. From that point on, people only saw beauty when they looked at her.

Elvis also spread an infectious love spell as did many others, and the fact is, you can, too.

———————

For more information on love spells and to receive your very own personalized love spell, send $20 along and a Self-Addressed Stamped Envelope to:

Rebel Girl Love Spells

P.O. Box Love in a Bottle

Nashville, TN 37204

Warning: Do not send the cash unless you are truly ready to find a match made in heaven.

Double warning: Ingredients not included, but they can be obtained by one who is truly seeking a love match.

Triple warning: Do not share your spell. It will cut all the effects of the love spell in half.

This is a one-time spell.

No refunds.

Dinosaurs

I tell myself back in the dinosaur days you could be walking down the street on your way to work, just minding your own business and suddenly there is a giant dinosaur flying above your head. He doesn't care if you are skinny or fat. He doesn't care if you're broke or rich. He doesn't care what your hair or your clothes look like or whether you took a shower. All he cares about is breakfast, and you are it. Think about that the next time you want to feel sorry for yourself.

(Use the space below to add more things dinosaurs don't care about.)

I'm for Love

I'm for love. The kind that makes "I love you" fly out of my mouth at random and strange moments in Tourette's-style Shakespearean sonnets.

I'm for love I can't shake off. Love that travels on my person everywhere I go, like my bones, like my head, like my feet.

I'm for love that doesn't need to be justified, or sanctified, or organized in albums by month and year to know I got it.

I'm for love that looks like a birthday cake and burns like baby oil at the beach.

I'm for love that doesn't tell me it's love. I know it is because the blood pumping through my heart is running off to tell my kidneys and my liver, "That chick is gone baby gone."

I'm for love I can detect with every perception: its location, its vibration, its sound, its touch.

I'm for love that pulls happy tears out of my eyes and runs waterfalls down my checks.

I'm for love I don't have to talk my mind into believing to make it bona fide.

I'm for love that I can't give up, even when it's ugly rough. Because I know the hell I am in is nothing compared to the damage the cannonball will leave inside my heart should I destroy it and yank it apart.

I'm for love that gives all and needs nothing. Love so big, it loves itself.

I'm for relentless, undying, never sacrifice it, no need to think twice about it, give you everything I got, lip satisfying, and soul-gratifying, everlasting love.

Everlasting, everlasting, everlasting love.

Air Machines and Squirt Guns

Let's take every drop of love we can find, push it into a big pile and jump in. How about we scoop it into buckets and pass it out to anybody who wants some? Let's dump it into gas station air machines and let people fill their tires with it. Let's paint it onto houses and highways. We could even stuff it into pillows and smash each other with them. Why don't we put it in squirt guns and soak everybody? (Add your ideas of what else we could do with it below.)

Technicolor Stardust Bubbles

I get inspired at around three in the morning when the rest of the world is sleeping. It seems like people start getting careless with their dreams about that time, and dreams begin floating down my street.

I sit on my front steps and watch them drift by in technicolor stardust bubbles. It's a good way to find out what kind of neighbors I have and if they have any imagination.

One time I saw the dream bubble of an eighth grader who lives next door to me. He was riding a giraffe down an aisle in Walmart and singing "I Will Always Love You" into an empty cardboard wrapping-paper tube.

I liked him a whole lot more after I saw that.

Tough Shit

Can a girl write love poems

or is that supposed to be left to men?

Can she say her heart fills

with the sweet whisper of lilacs

when she hears his name?

Can she tell the world that his touch

is sweeter than the thought of heaven?

Can she say if heaven were offered,

she would deny it in exchange for his kiss?

Would you find her too forward

or brash for writing about him?

Tough shit.

Plastic Ruby Ring

Gumball machine plastic ruby ring, you are the prettiest thing I've ever seen. You cost me a quarter and lasted three days. Such a deal, such a steal, you made me feel like you were real. I might go back and buy me another one. Turning the crank is half the fun and besides that, I love you.

Love Gets Better

Love gets better, don't get bitter.

Bitter won't make it better.

Better won't make it bitter.

There are lots of people in the world

who want to love somebody.

There are billions of people who want to be loved.

Let them in.

Forever

I've survived first love, true love, and real love. I've been through love hurts and love sucks. I've done love will tear you to pieces and I don't think anyone will ever truly love me.

I've lived through love is killing me, love is over, and love is dead. I've had my heart ripped out of my chest several times.

Somehow, I've made it to the river of deep love. The till-death-do-us-part love.

Not because I said, "I do," in front of a bunch of our family and friends, either. That was nothing. Those were just Words, and I really didn't even know what they meant at the time.

It's till death do us part now because I'm in so deep there is no way out. I'm in so deep my soul is his soul and his soul is mine. I'm so far in I don't ever want to love anybody else.

So, I'm hanging on as tight as I can for as long as I can.

Because I know that one day, I won't have that option, no matter what I do, and because I want to give, and I want to take every drop of this love with me.

So, I can remember it for all time.

Forever.

Enough

He makes my eyes feel like flowers.

Bright bursting petals of orange and pink fire.

He makes my hands feel like water,

fluid and graceful.

I do not know what it means.

I do not care.

It is enough.

The Beatles, Soldiers, and Love

Billions of voices used to travel through telephone wires every day. All of the "I'm on my way home now" and "Would you tell her I called" still hang from the copper. When you get close, you can hear the echo of teenage girls making plans to go see the Beatles and homesick soldiers calling up their mothers to wish them Happy Birthday.

You can even hear newspapermen reporting old stories about Muhammad Ali and George Foreman. Vivid tales of Lindbergh, the *Titanic*, and Watergate, the World Trade Center, Martin Luther King Jr., the moon landing, Bonnie and Clyde, D-Day, Kurt Cobain, Billie Holiday, Henry Ford, Judy Garland, Babe Ruth, Bill Clinton, Michael Jordan, etc., etc., etc. Many of the souls are gone, but not the voices.

Of course, there are millions of people who have never given up the ring dialing. They say, "That's the way I've always done it, I am not changing now." Every school and most businesses continue to talk through the phone lines. But one day, it's going to be over and all that wire and all those transmitters will be relics, just like the typewriter, the calculator, and the phone booth.

It makes me wonder about certain things. Things like, whose voice will be the last voice to vibrate through the lines? Like, will the last voice and the last words ever spoken live inside the metal wires infinitely, on and on and on and on?

I think they will. That is why I am hoping the final words going through those old telephone lines will be the most sincere and truthful "I love you" ever spoken.

So even after every wire is pulled down and crushed or buried in the earth, we will still feel that last bit of love that flowed through the wires flowing right out into the world, on and on and on...

20/20 Vision Truth

You light my universe up with shimmering 20/20 vision truth. I can see who I am meant to be when we are one.

Never would I give you up. Never would I desert you.

You are the mercy of a thousand gods who looked down upon my tragic heart and bequeathed you to me.

You are my treasure, my beautiful world, my ever and for always.

No trip to the sky could ever convince me that heaven has not always been and will always be you.

Love Letter

When I die, I will not die quickly, I will fly away slowly. I am not afraid. Death is no more real than a Hollywood movie. Although a very sad movie, indeed. But I know that after my body takes its last breath I will live again. Just like Buddha did, just like Jesus, just like you.

Everyone lives forever, of course. We all disappear and come back pretending we have never been here before. It's like filing for bankruptcy, the slate is wiped clean.

I hope we find each other again every couple of hundred years or so. We will both get that "I feel like I've known you before" feeling. We will have those, *you seem very familiar to me* thoughts. But we will call it *love at first sight*. Like we have so many times before.

This Petal's Home

If our universe was one of the petals on a giant flower,

and if all the other petals were other universes,

we could say,

"This petal's home."

You might not want to say it, but I would.

I would say it every day. All the time.

When someone said, "The world is horrible,

I don't know what is going on in the world."

I would say,

"This petal's home."

Forget It

"I love thee, is that not enough?" he asked.

"No," she said.

"Must I pull the moon down from the sky and move the Milky Way for you? Must I cover the ground where you step with gold bangles? Must I climb mountains and slay dragons in your name? Must I destroy your grief and protect your dreams to prove my love to you?" he asked.

"Yes," she said.

"Why?" he asked.

"Forget it," she said. "It doesn't count if you have to ask.

Memories

Sometimes

memories

sneak

out

of

my

eyes

and

roll

down

my

cheeks.

My Favorite Color

Your soul is beautiful. It is my favorite color.

Please don't dye it.

I might not recognize you when we meet again.

Just kidding, I'd know your soul in any color.

I'd know your soul in the dark.

I'd know your soul if it didn't have a body.

I don't need my eyes to find you.

I know you.

I know you in my soul.

Public Service Announcement #2

Do not stare into the eyes of cute little glass bears. Do not stare at fuzzy bears, cookie-jar bears, crystal bears, china-bears or kissable bears painted on the side of tin canisters, etc. They look all innocent, but they are not.

They are hypnotizing agents of the cruel Cuddly Wuddly Clan. Within minutes of holding one or looking into its eyes, you will find yourself feeling sentimental and unloved.

These bears will give you a crippling desire to be taken care of and the false perception that you are unable to stand on your own two feet. It may sound crazy, but I swear it's true.

If you have ever found yourself wishing you could be some sort of fairy princess, you may have previously been exposed to the evil Cuddly Wuddly trickery.

To awaken yourself from this harmful trance, hang upside from a tree branch. The higher the branch, the quicker the remedy. Do not come down from the branch until you no longer feel unloved.

If this sounds ridiculous to you but you have the desire to be a fragile, *please take care of me princess*, the Cuddly Wuddly trance has you locked in tight. To loosen its grip, fill your bathtub with ice and seven inches of water. Then lie in it until you wake up. You will know you are awake when the idea of being a princess makes you want to puke.

These are the only safe remedies for this sneaky hypnotic trance. Seek no other cure if you want to live.

Heed these warnings and follow these instructions closely if you have any signs of Cuddly Wuddly contamination.

The war is on.

Stop giving your power to the Cuddly Wuddly Clan and be the badass you were born to be.

Don't ever let a little knickknack kick your ass.

Glory

There is nothing quite like being yourself.

No matter what.

In all your freak-flag glory.

In all of your beautiful, one-of-a-kind,

perfectly perfect, never-been-seen-before perfection.

Bring it on.

(Write what is awesome about you in the space below. If you

need more room, get another piece of paper and keep going.)

Be Normal

If you don't like being called weird or strange, be normal. If you prefer not to stick out, not to get loud, be normal.

If you don't like to move your hands up and down and shout across a crowded crowd, to get the attention of a friend or someone you just met or someone you would like to meet, I repeat, be normal.

If you fear people noticing that you are different. If good for you is blending in. If you need to be accepted, protected, if you don't want to rock the boat, and can't take rejection, be normal.

If you need everyone to love you. If you hold other people's opinion of you, above you. If you don't mind letting people push and shove you and tug you, so you can only go where they want you to go, be normal.

If you don't care about having your own opinion. If you don't mind being a minion to bullies and pricks again and again.

If you are into running with the pack, wolves on your back, never knowing where you're at, never knowing where you stand, never knowing if you can, be normal.

Score

I wish I could breathe underwater like a fish. Like truly have the physical ability to live underwater for as long as I wanted. Not because I want to live underwater or hang out there or anything. But just so I could say that I can breathe underwater if the subject of breathing underwater ever comes up in conversation. I could be like, "I can breathe underwater." Score.

Darkness

The darkness was deep.

People climbed down for days searching to find out why.

Some tried to get the darkness to speak.

They were looking for answers for sorrow and madness.

Others pleaded with the darkness to give them peace.

After a long search, some decided they didn't need any answers. They needed light.

So, they climbed up and out into the sunshine.

I am not going to say it cured them of their sorrow.

But it was much easier for them to see.

Black and White World

What if there were no colors in the world and everything was black and white? Black and white animals, black and white people, black and white trees, roads, and buildings, handbags, golf clubs, flowers, fields, rivers, oceans, and skies of only black and white?

What if emotion was black and white, and happiness was black and white, and affection was black and white? Could you take it? I can hardly think about it. I wouldn't want to listen to black and white music or read black and white books.

I couldn't fall in black and white love. No, I need color to see where I am and what is what. I need color to get my own perspective and to know what I think.

I need the bright yellow sunrise and the tall green grass at the edge of a clear blue pond. I need purple plums, red leaves, red lipstick, and the cherry flush in a baby's cheeks. I need to know there is Orange Crush, orange juice, and orange Converse All Stars available if I so desire them.

What about the pink in a cat's nose, pink bowling balls, pink flamingos, and pink Cadillacs? I need *all* the colors in the box of crayons and every other hue as well.

I need colors to feel the different shades of people's hearts. I need color to hear the tones in music and words. And can you imagine a black and white kiss? I'd rather not be kissed at all.

No, I would not like thinking in only black and white thoughts and seeing only black and white views and knowing only black and white hope.

So, if it ever happens, if we ever find ourselves in a black and white world and you don't like it, look for me.

I'll be searching for the door and the dye.

Floating

I float in my sleep.

I float up walls and across canyons.

Sometimes I can't move, I can't speak,

I am being pulled by something I know not what.

It's disturbing.

When I wake up, I know I've traveled many miles.

But if I tell anyone they say, "That's just a dream."

And I say, "Yeah," but I don't believe it.

Everything Has a Double

Almost everything in this universe has a double. Somethings even have a triple. But most of the time you can't see it. Yesterday, I saw the sun's double when the two of them slipped apart. They didn't know that I was looking, or they just got lazy and separated for a moment. I am sure it's hard to be stuck together all the time.

All the same, I did get a picture of it and I'd sell the picture to *Life* magazine if I thought they would believe me. But you know how they are. They'd get someone in there debunking my photo and my theory. Just like they do with every cool discovery people make, such as Bigfoot sightings, spaceships, aliens, natural cures, etc.

That's why I am writing about it. To make a record of it. To record the sighting. I took a picture of it with my iPhone over by the one and only Trader Joe's in Nashville, TN. The photo has not been edited or filtered in any way. So just know when you see it that you are looking at our sun's double no matter what anyone says about it.

Maybe you will catch the two suns slip apart in person someday. Or maybe you will catch the moon's double or the Grand Canyon's. I hope you do. The universe is full of secrets. It's always fun to find one.

(Use this space to write a secret you have discovered about the universe.)

Jones Beach

Last July, Lucy met an intensely attractive man-boy at Jones Beach. He was sitting on the pier wrapped in lean, tan muscle and shorts. His smile revealed perfectly straight, if slightly large, white teeth.

He was the kind of guy who would never have spoken to a pleasantly plain, freckled, cherry-head like Lucy.

The wind was mild that day yet hearty enough to carry the powerful voodoo love spell she quickly concocted out of rainbow slivers and drops of sleeping fairy breath. Lucy always carries love spell ingredients in her almost-real Louis Vuitton bag for just such an occasion.

After mixing the spell, she blew it off of her hand and watched it flutter before landing on the breeze that carried it to him. Its effect was immediate, and he began falling over himself to learn Lucy's name the moment the concoction blew through his sandy blond hair.

By mid-September, he was proposing to her daily. Now, once a week they walk into the cottage boutiques on Madison Avenue. Boutiques that Lucy would never have walked into before because they are shockingly overpriced and snobby.

The counter girls give Lucy free clothes because they think she is rich. Only rich girls or beautiful girls date such impressive men. Lucy always says, "Thank you," when she accepts a free cashmere sweater or a pair of sailor-cut linen slacks. But she never ever says it so gratuitously that one would know she has the power to cast voodoo love spells.

For further information on concocting your own love spell, please send a single $20 bill and a Self-Addressed Stamped Envelope to the address below.

———————

Rebel Girl Love Spells

P.O. Box Love in a Bottle

Nashville, TN 37204

<u>Warning</u>: Do not send the cash unless you are truly ready to find a match made in heaven.

<u>Double warning</u>: Ingredients not included but they can be obtained by one who is truly seeking a love match.

<u>Triple warning</u>: Do not share your spell with anyone. It will cut all the effects of the love spell in half.

<u>Caution</u>: This is a one-time spell.

No refunds.

Venus

Two months ago, I wrote my name on Venus. I went out into space and wrote my name as big as I could on a flag and left it there. I used a neon green Sharpie hoping you might be able to see it from Earth. But you can't.

Some people have told me they have seen it with a telescope. But I know they are just saying that to make me feel good. So that's nice and all, but it's not true, and if there's one thing I can't stand, it's a lie.

Now I have to go back up there with a bunch of organic neon pink spray paint and spray my name as big as I can on the side of the planet. Look for it. I'm hoping that will work.

Peace

I'm for peace.

I'm for peace as something to keep. Peace that stops a
heart bleed, peace that sets you free.

I'm for peace that lets people be who they want to be.

I'm for peace, the kind you feel after making love when
your body and soul feel in communion with the world
of sweet contentment.

I'm for peace that puts a mind at ease. The way it does
after confessing to a small or large regrettable act: such
as stealing a candy bar or denting a fender or robbing a
bank.

I'm for peace that doesn't come after war. I'm for peace
instead of war. I'm for peace that is declared as loudly

as war is declared. I'm for a president coming on the TV stating, "I declare peace! Live by it or spend your days cleaning up the trash on the side of the highway!"

I'm for peace pipes, not weed pipes making money killing brain cells, filling jail cells, but that's just me, saying what I see. You do what you please, with your head with your dreams.

I'm for peace.

The Secret Bridge

There is a secret bridge above the trees near our house. It is completely invisible unless you are wearing some counteractive Secret Bridge Visible Glasses, which we own.

We like to hang out up there after midnight a couple of nights a week because that is when it gets interesting. The bridge has a super-turbocharger type of vacuum built into its structure. It's one of a kind, as far as I know.

I cannot tell you the specifics of exactly how it works, because that is something I do not know. But if you don't want to get sucked out into the universe when you are up there, you have to wear a pair of heavy steel-vacuum, defense boots and chain them to a steel barrier, which we do. When I say we, I mean me and Bob.

The machine comes on at 12:30 a.m. We stand on one side of the bridge and watch the paraphernalia that is getting sucked off the Earth that night. Everything I have seen getting pulled up is something you wouldn't want anyway. Which is good, because there is no way to stop it once it gets caught in the pull.

At first, the stuff moves leisurely down a large tube into a clear capsule that's about the size of three big dump trucks. Once the capsule is full, everything goes silent for a minute or two and then somehow, everything in the capsule turns to glitter and gets shot out into space. I swear they make stars with that machine. I have observed several of the constellations growing brighter over the last few years.

There are all types of objects that get caught in the pull. Everything from parking tickets to bombs. We see a lot of thought bubbles getting sucked up there, too. Thoughts like *I hate myself* or *the world is doomed,* and *nobody loves me* are fairly common.

The thought bubbles scream and moan on their way into the capsule. Which makes sense to me, because if you have ever spoken with a negative person, you know they go on and on like there is no end to the bad news and you just want to cover your ears before you fall to pieces, too.

We have also encountered such things as torture and murder in the vacuum. It's not that we have seen anyone being tortured or murdered. But we see shadow images of it. Once you do see images like that, all you want is to see them disappear forever.

Those activities have particular wavelengths. These waves are so violent, you can feel the pain and death running through your own body. Sometimes, you even feel like you are dying yourself. But when that wave has made its way through the vacuum and out to wherever it goes, I have noticed I personally feel lighter. Lighter than I did before I ever felt it in the vacuum.

It's amazing, it's like we are personally feeling the world feel better.

So, if you think the world is bad right now, you would not believe what it would be like if that vacuum was shut off. I think it must have been built to keep us afloat against the destruction that has hit us almost unendingly since time began.

I have no idea who built it or how long it's been there. But it is old. It might even be thousands of years old. I am pretty sure it has Egyptian hieroglyphics on it, along with pictures people have drawn onto the surface. Everything from cowboys on horses to people burning at the stake are painted or etched into the structure.

I hope no one is ever able to stop the vacuum. I like knowing the ugliness is getting sucked away. Of course, it can't get everything, just like a vacuum can't get all the dirt out of the carpet. But it can get a lot of it.

That tells you how much more shit we would have going on in our world than we know. As far as I can tell, we are only experiencing the stuff that didn't get sucked out in the vacuum, and that thing runs every night, all night long.

Reading Minds

I've got one green eye and one blue eye. That's why I'm good at reading people's minds.

(Use the space below to write what color eyes you have and what you can do.)

Rhythm

Rhythm, I feel you in everything.

You are omnipresent.

You roll out of tires and pulse in kissing lips.

What a reckless world it would be

without your groove, without your beat.

Beauty would be lost in a cacophony of indecision.

The Earth would hurl jerkily through space,

and we'd all be bad dancers who clapped offbeat

to music that played out of time.

Give me rhythm or give me death.

My Shit

I lost my shit last Friday and I don't want it back. I've carried that crap around for years without even knowing I had it. If you find it, you can keep it. But don't bring it back to me, I don't want it. If I had realized what it was, I would have gotten rid of it sooner.

Wasted Time

I

think

about

how

much

time

I

have

wasted.

Then I think what a waste of time it was

to think about that.

Brakes

She had her foot on the brake and couldn't figure out why she wasn't moving.

Explanation:

She wasn't really in a car, and her foot was not on an actual brake. This is just a figure of speech to say she was going nowhere but could not understand why. It's saying she didn't notice she was the one stopping herself. She was the one keeping herself in place and she was in a state of wonder as to why she wasn't getting anywhere.

Sarcasm:

This is a myth type of concept. Things like this never happen. It's just something I made up, so people could see that someone in a fiction book might do this in a story. Nobody ever encounters this type of situation in real life. But sometimes it makes for an interesting, if not frustrating, theme in a book.

Super-Short Scary Story

I saw something in the window of an abandoned house.

A light, a flicker, an old woman in a black dress.

She waved for me to come closer.

I did not move.

I knew she had died seven years earlier.

I went to her funeral.

Stuff in My Head

Dime-store photographs sell for $2, but nobody ever looks at the rack anymore. It's only smoke and mirrors anyway, and sometimes it's mirrors and smoke. You know it's hard to choke on the truth when everybody has a different version of what the truth is. Don't take it too seriously though, it's all just words and I got a lot of stuff in my head.

Stars and Dreams

I took a dream and I folded it in half, then in quarters and eighths. Then I went to the garage and got a pair of scissors; that's what I call them anyway. My guess is they were more like a pair of branch cutters, but you get the idea. Anyway, I cut stars and a moon and a sun into that folded-up dream.

When I was done, I unfolded it from eighths to quarters, to halves and then back to the whole. At that point, I got the biggest brightest spotlight I could find and stuck the dream over the top of that blinding beam.

Now you know how I made the sun, the moon, and the stars. As you can guess, a bunch of other planets found their way in too. You know, because of the folding thing? So, my little old dream turned into a whole galaxy.

That will be 25 cents. Please leave it in the bucket on your way out the door.

Popular has never been as cool, as cool.

The Weeds

Sometimes

I sit in the weeds

and pretend they are flowers.

Okay, almost all the time.

Pillows in the Sky

So, my name is listed in the one and only *Guinness Book of World Records*. Not because I wanted it in there, but because I built a mile-high cotton mountain out of pillows, so I could hang out up there with the clouds. It took me 10 whole years to collect enough pillows. Most were donated by people who thought I would never do it, but I did not care. I needed every pillow I could get.

See, I wanted to get a view of the world from a cloud's perspective, and my intention was to try and casually fit in. I thought it would be cool to relax up there for a bit without intruding on the chill vibe the clouds have going on a lazy summer day.

In order to create that atmosphere, I filled the peak of my mountain with the lightest, whitest, and fluffiest pillows I could find. The pillows below them were covered with light blue cases so they would blend into the baby blue sky.

It was not easy throwing, stacking, and climbing up, I can tell you that for sure. But I did hire several high school shop students to help me with the construction and after 12 days of long, sweaty work, I finally found myself among the billows with a gorgeous view of the world below me. It was pure bliss for about 15 minutes. After that, the clouds started talking to each other.

Believe me, it was as surprising to me to hear them speak as I am sure it is to you to hear they spoke. Probably even more so. The biggest shock was that their voices were not soft and wispy like you would imagine a cloud's voice should be. Some were loud and whiny like a spoiled kid who did not get what he wanted for his birthday. You cannot imagine how chatty these clouds were. It all looks so peaceful up there from the ground, but I can assure you it is not.

I ended up listening to one long commentary after another about what was going on down below. It sounded like a news report with loud intermittent interjections about cloud personal problems. One cloud had a football broadcaster voice and ran a play-by-play on what was happening with a traffic backup on a highway below us. Another cloud was nervous about some kids playing ball in the street and kept shouting, "Car, car!"

If you can imagine what a wallflower cloud would look and sound like, well I met one of those, too. She started complaining about a love relationship that was ripped apart by a strong breeze. I was told she had been grieving about losing her true love for seven years.

It sounds like I'm kidding, but seriously, this is no joke. And here's another revelation: Clouds are extremely self-conscious. I met several that were worried about being fat and I spoke with a few who were on diets and diuretics because they were retaining too much water. I tried to explain to them the purpose and science of clouds. They weren't interested, and I ended up spending most of my time consoling them. I was up there telling them, "You're perfect just the way you are."

I crossed my heart and told them people admire them. I said artists spend countless hours trying to paint them. That poets go insane searching for just the right words to describe them. I even confessed that people spend endless amounts of time looking up at them and wishing they could take one home.

They said they had no idea we even think about them at all. Except to curse them on a rainy day or to demand their shade when the sun is hot.

They strongly dislike the way we fly through them in planes and said it's uncomfortable to be separated like that. One sensitive cloud asked me how I would like it if a plane flew through me.

They said they hate it when we lay on the ground and point at them and say they look like a dog or a pig. To tell you the whole truth, I was relieved to come down. It was definitely more romantic to think about sitting up there with the clouds than it actually was to sit up there. I started to feel just terrible because I knew I was going to become a person who is down on clouds.

I keep telling myself, maybe I was up there at a bad time. Maybe they were having a bad day. I honestly never felt so stressed out in my life, and after several hours I began my long, difficult climb back down.

As I descended, I heard some chuckling that soon turned into big, hearty laughter. I knew they were laughing at me because one of them blurted, "Humans will believe anything." It didn't take long before they were all singing, "I want to rock and roll all night and party every day."

I was feeling very discouraged when a crow flew past me and whispered, "Keep your head out of the clouds."

I knew exactly what he meant.

Big Old Knot

I was at the end of my rope.

So, I grabbed another rope and tied the two of them together in a big old knot.

Now I'm like, "No problem."

Now I'm like, "Bring it on."

Now I'm like, "Is that all you got?"

Light Years

She brushed her cheeks with star-shine so even the sky would see her glow. Years later, when the Milky Way galaxy finally saw her light, she was sitting in the bathroom at McDonald's texting a friend about how invisible she feels.

Public Service Announcement #3

"You're nobody till somebody loves you."

This is a great song.

But it's a total lie.

Alabaster Shards

We walk through a field of alabaster shards

and bits of ebony.

No one notices the spirits in the trees,

but I hear them singing hallelujah.

I do not know if they are happy

or just following the leader.

Immortal

I want to be immortal and play hopscotch on the steps of time. Every time I die, I want to remember where I left all my best stuff, so I can sell it in my next life and travel all through my twenties. I want to tell people they will live forever, and when I see the fear and the dread coming over their face at the thought of living forever, I want to tell them: It's okay, we are all in the same boat.

Zeus

I met Zeus in a dream last night. But it didn't quite feel like a dream because Zeus plucked me out of my bed with his giant hand and pulled me right up to his face. Then he asked me if I believed in him. He was right there so what could I say but, "Yes."

"Good, then I must exist," he said.

I must exist, too, I thought.

How strange it is for a god to verify his existence with me. Perhaps it was just me verifying my existence with a god. But I don't think so.

Here

If you are here, I'll be here to notice that you are here. And you will know you exist because I will tell you that I see you.

I will know I exist because you will be there to see me.

Not everyone needs such reassurances, but then not everyone is awake enough to see the dream.

Lifetimes

I plan on living a long life.

I like being me.

I will miss who I am when I die

and come back with a new face

and a new name.

I am having one of my favorite lifetimes.

(Use this space to write what a favorite lifetime would have.)

Black Sheep Rebel Girl

She doesn't belong to this world. She doesn't belong to any world. She wasn't made out of sun rays or stardust or moonbeams. She was created from nothing but the hard truth of forever. There is no part of her in the flesh or the bone that makes the body she wears. But she pretends she's only human. Just like everyone else.

Black Sheep Rebel Girl

We climb clouds.

Black Sheep Rebel Girl

The floor was made of eggshells.

We put our combat boots on.

It wasn't made of eggshells for long.

Mars

If everyone left earth to live on Mars or some space station and I were left down here alone, I would still write. I would write stories and songs even if there were no people to read them or to sing them. For *I* would read them, and *I* would sing them. I think it would help me feel less lonely and pissed off that all you bastards left me down here all by myself.

Sidewalk

I put my ear on the sidewalk, so I can hear what it is thinking.

It never says anything but "Get off me."

Same with the road.

So, I Did

"We are who we are, no use crying about it," I said to myself for no particular reason at all. It just sounded good in my head, and I thought I should write it down.

So, I did.

Love Potion

One day, I dipped the tip of an arrow

into a contagious love potion

and shot it into a patch of clouds.

Then I did a rain dance.

It poured for weeks.

All kinds of people fell in love.

The End.

Join my mailing list for updates

and to get your FREE

Black Sheep Rebel Girl Mini Book with extra Rebel
Girl stories, thoughts, and observations.

www.rachelhutchesonwriter.com

Thank you so much for reading my book!

Did you enjoy it?

Reviews and word of mouth are the most powerful tools I have when it comes to getting attention for my books. Honest reviews of my books help bring them to the attention of other readers.

If you enjoyed this book, I would be most grateful if you would spend a few minutes leaving me a review on Amazon. It can be as short as you like. Thank you!

Also by Rachel Hutcheson

The Black Sheep Rebel Girl Rises Again
Whimsical Tales and Truthful Lies

The Black Sheep Rebel Girl Rises Again offers a whimsical freewheeling collection of stories and writings about crazy love, truthful lies, and the power of being yourself. Follow the Rebel Girl as she shares tales, thoughts, and discoveries on love, loyalty, heartbreak, friendship, loneliness, bravery, perseverance, and more.

"I am the first daughter of a rattlesnake wrestling princess named Lily Pond-Pond and a funny king we called "My Vote Counts for Five." Once I tore a hole in the sky and almost got sucked out of the universe. When you tell people stories like this, they think you are kidding, so I pretend I write fiction. The truth is I have never written a word of fiction in my life. Everything I write is almost absolutely true..." -Rachel Hutcheson, *The Black Sheep Rebel Girl Rises Again*

This funny and thought-provoking collection is for anyone who wants to feel inspired. It is for the free-spirit heart and the heart that wants to get back its free-spirit.

The Black Sheep Rebel Girl Rises Again is the second book in the delightful Black Sheep Rebel Girl collection. If you like to laugh, if you like out-of-the-box stories, and feeling good, you will love this book.

Pick up *The Black Sheep Rebel Girl Rises Again* today!

·

Acknowledgements

I would like to give a big thank you to:

My friend Devon Heath for encouraging me to write this book.

My sweet husband Bob Hutcheson for his endless love, help, and support.

My strong, and beautiful mother for never failing to believe in me and for giving me her love, wisdom and life.

My friend Lori White for her excellent suggestions, encouragement, good-eye and help.

Rachel Hutcheson is an award-winning songwriter, writer, and performer. She received a degree in theatre from Western Michigan University and spent many years performing in Los Angeles and New York. Rachel currently lives in Nashville, TN with her husband, who she met at a party in college. It was true love. It was love-at-first sight.

Made in the USA
Monee, IL
25 November 2022